7

8

9

10

D0297436

11

12

£2.65

Judy FOR GIRLS

Printed and Published in Great Britain by D. C. Thomson & Co., Ltd., 185 Fleet Street, London EC42 2HS. © D. C. THOMSON & CO., LTD., 1986
ISBN 0-85116-362-9.

A Helping Hand

ANGELA'S family had decided to spend the summer holiday on lonely Windel Moor. At her first sight of the remote cottage they had rented, Angela sensed an atmosphere about it.

It's lovely . . . but . . . but there's something sad about the place. Can't you feel it? It's as if something tragic once happened here.

She's off again, Penny!

"One evening a thick mist sprang up. She feared he'd lost his way in the swamp."

Jem! Je-em, can you hear me?

The taxi driver was from the nearby village.

But the young lady's right. Over a hundred years ago, a young girl called Jenny Seager lived here. She loved a boy in our village, and each evening he crossed the swamp that used to be here to see her.

And . . . and what happened?

"Their poor, drowned bodies were recovered days later, miles from each other. People round here say you can still hear Jenny sometimes at night, calling her Jem."

But Jem had wandered to the other end of the swamp, and they never did find each other.

5

As the panto[m]
unfolds, the hero[es]
heroines win thei[r]
to riches, weddin[g]
living happily eve[r]

Pantomimes have gradually evolved over many years from an older form of entertainment called a harlequinade. The word pantomime means "dumb-show" — acting without any use of words — and the harlequinade began as a kind of play acted in mime.

There were certain stock characters in every harlequinade. They were Harlequin, Pierrot, Columbine and Pantaloon. Very gradually, fairy stories and nursery tales came to be used for the opening scenes of the harlequinade and, during the 19th century, the entertainment that had first been designed for grown-ups, changed to a treat mainly for children.

ARUNDEL CASTLE

Recently, we asked Clare to visit Arundel Castle where she had a most enjoyable day.

"Nearly there."

"Well! Well!"

"Wonder if this drawbridge still works."

"He's not aMOOsed!"

"One last look."

15

DORIA
AND THE
DEMON

HAVE you ever wanted something so much that you'd do anything to achieve your ambition? Doria Page felt like that about gaining a place in the county swimming team. The trouble was, Doria couldn't swim fast enough.

Sorry, Dor... ...y, though.

A good try? What use is that?

Later—

Forget it, Doria. Who wants to be in the county team anyway?

...e selected!

17

18

During the last week of term, Doria trained hard for the swimming events, but—

I'm second — still not good enough!

Later—

You've improved a lot, Doria, but don't be too disappointed if you don't get into the team this year.

How can I help being disappointed?

On the way home—

Look at it this way, Doria, it's better to lose than to do a deal with a demon!

Suddenly—

Hello again! I've got a great deal for you! As many years as you like, and a guaranteed selection for the team!

DEMON'S PATENT BLOOD

WASHABLE, GUARANTEED NOT TO RUN. — 25 P —

DEMON'S PATENT BLOOD

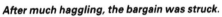

After much haggling, the bargain was struck.

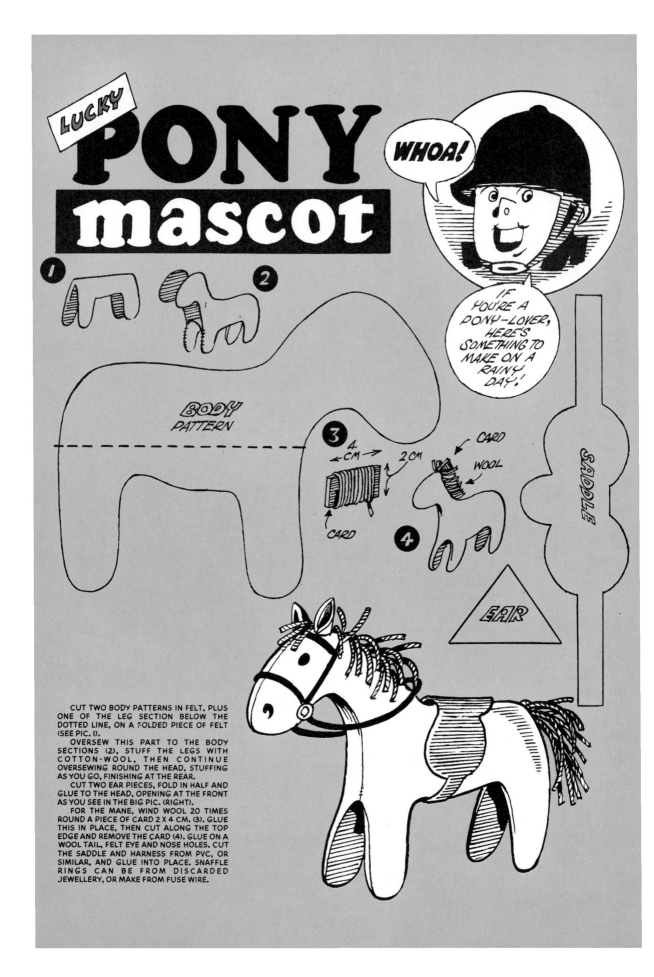

LUCKY PONY mascot

WHOA!

IF YOU'RE A PONY-LOVER, HERE'S SOMETHING TO MAKE ON A RAINY DAY!

CUT TWO BODY PATTERNS IN FELT, PLUS ONE OF THE LEG SECTION BELOW THE DOTTED LINE, ON A FOLDED PIECE OF FELT (SEE PIC. I).

OVERSEW THIS PART TO THE BODY SECTIONS (2), STUFF THE LEGS WITH COTTON-WOOL, THEN CONTINUE OVERSEWING ROUND THE HEAD, STUFFING AS YOU GO, FINISHING AT THE REAR.

CUT TWO EAR PIECES, FOLD IN HALF AND GLUE TO THE HEAD, OPENING AT THE FRONT AS YOU SEE IN THE BIG PIC. (RIGHT).

FOR THE MANE, WIND WOOL 20 TIMES ROUND A PIECE OF CARD 2 X 4 CM. (3). GLUE THIS IN PLACE, THEN CUT ALONG THE TOP EDGE AND REMOVE THE CARD (4). GLUE ON A WOOL TAIL, FELT EYE AND NOSE HOLES. CUT THE SADDLE AND HARNESS FROM PVC, OR SIMILAR, AND GLUE INTO PLACE. SNAFFLE RINGS CAN BE FROM DISCARDED JEWELLERY, OR MAKE FROM FUSE WIRE.

THE PLANT

SHELLEY VALE just couldn't stop meddling with other people's property. Her mother was always telling her about it.

Ooops! I've spilt Mum's perfume!

Oh, golly! Didn't mean to tear the book!

RIIPPP

Gran'dad's watch! I was only winding it!

That does it! Go to your room and stay out of mischief until tea-time!

SPROING!

24

But it's been a lesson to me! I swear I'll never meddle with other people's things again!

And Shelley kept her word — for at least a week.

Shelley, do you feel all right? You've been sitting there all night without once fiddling with my sewing basket!

I-er-I'm just not interested in sewing baskets, Mum.

But, a few days later—

Shelley! There goes my change all over the floor!

One morning—

Mr Biggs told me that he's being transferred up North. So we'll be looking for a new lodger.

Yes — well, let's hope he doesn't spend hours in the bathroom like Biggs does!

Funny — I felt a bit cold when Mum said that. Wonder why?

The new lodger arrived two weeks later.

Let's help the professor in with his stuff, Shelley — then we'll make a cup of tea.

Professor?

How do you do, Mrs Vale? I wonder if you have a suitably humid room for my Venus Fly Trap. I'm rather attached to it.

The attic will be perfect for it, Professor Trent. In fact, you could keep all your scientific things there.

Thank you, Mrs Vale. I'm sure the plant is going to thrive here as it's never thrived before.

27

THE END

29

JUNIOR NANNY

It's a lovely morning, Edward. Wouldn't you like to play in the garden with the other children?

CHRIS JOHNSON worked at a residential nursery for the under-fives. Edward, who was four and an orphan, had been brought up by his only relative, an elderly great-aunt. When she died, Edward was sent to the nursery.

No, thank you, Nurse Chris.

It's nice and quiet in here, and I'm not lonely because I have William to keep me company.

He adores that teddy, but he does need to get used to the company of other kids.

Our cleaning lady wants to get on with her work in here, Edward. Come along — the fresh air will do you good.

All right. I'll just put my drawing things away.

My word, Edward, you are a tidy little boy.

Aunt Jane liked everything to be tidy.

Too tidy, I reckon.

See what fun the boys are having?

I think I'll just watch for now, Nurse.

Well, I've coaxed Edward into the garden, Anne. Here's hoping he decides to take the plunge and join in the fun.

It would certainly do him good. He's far too serious for a child of four.

A few minutes later—

Please, Nurse Chris, a boy bounced the ball up and it hit me and made a dirty mark on my shirt. I...I'm sorry.

It doesn't matter, Edward. Off you go and enjoy yourself.

I ... I can't. My shirt is dirty. It's not nice to get dirty.

It can be great fun, Edward. We don't expect you to keep clean all the time. We're not cross with you, so don't get upset.

But Edward began to cry.

It's not nice! It's not! I like to be clean and tidy!

Don't cry, Edward. Nurse, take him upstairs and change his shirt.

That's better. Now I'm all nice and clean again.

Poor Edward! I doubt that fussy aunt of his ever allowed him to romp around behaving like a normal little boy.

It's my day off tomorrow. I'll ask Matron if Andrew and I can take Edward out. He has taken to Andrew—most kids do.

Andrew, Chris's student boyfriend, lived at a hostel next door to the nursery.

The next day—

It's too soon for lunch, so let's have a paddle in the stream.

That's a good idea, Chris. Come on, Edward—socks and sandals off. It'll be fun.

Edward refused politely.

Change your mind, Edward, and give it a try. It really is fun.

The water is quite warm, Edward.

It might splash my clothes and I expect there's mud at the bottom of the stream. William and I will just watch.

A little later—

Come on, Edward! It's super fun to roly-poly, isn't it, Andrew?

Great! I'll bet you could be the champion roly-poly boy if you practised, Edward!

I shall just watch.

Edward ate his lunch standing up, in case he got grass stains on his trousers.

He even tries to eat extra neatly, and wipe his mouth between each bite! Ah well, we'll try some more games after lunch.

In the late afternoon—

Cheer up, love. We did our best.

But our best wasn't good enough.

He didn't join in the fun—and he's as neat and clean as when we set out.

The following evening—

Hopefully, that's the children settled down for the night. It's been a long day, with Anne off-duty.

Take a look at this. Edward gave it to me. It's a good effort for a four-year-old.

See? He's made William the king of the castle.

Mmm! I've an idea coming on . . .

Later—

. . . and Andrew is sure he can borrow the college's mini-bus for Saturday. What do you think, Matron?

It could work out well, considering how much Edward thinks of his teddy-bear.

On the Saturday morning—

All aboard for the Teddy-Bears' Seaside Outing!

The kids look so happy and excited—except for Edward. But I'm hoping that, before the day is out, he'll be wearing a big smile.

An hour or so later—

I want to paddle, Matron. I'll carry my teddy.

Paddling comes later, children. First we are going to build a big castle. When it is built, we'll choose a teddy to sit on top of it and be King of the Castle for the day.

Ooh!

I want to keep nice and clean, Nurse..so I won't be able to help. I think William would make the best king, though. He is a special bear.

I'm sure he is, Edward, but if you don't help build the castle, there's no chance of him being chosen. It wouldn't be fair.

Aunt Jane said good boys always stay neat and clean, but . . . Oh, William! I do love you very much, and I know you would like to be King of the Castle!

Later—

I think it's going to be a very good castle, Andrew.

So do I. You're putting in a lot of work into it, Edward.

And by the brightness in his eyes, he's enjoying himself . . . forgetting about staying neat and clean, and finding out what fun is.

William's bear was voted King of the Castle by the other children.

William is very pleased and proud at being chosen. I can tell. I'm so glad I helped to build the castle, Nurse Chris!

So am I, Edward. Now, we'll put our swimthings on and enjoy a paddle.

This is great fun, Nurse Chris!

And it's good to see Edward enjoying himself, at last.

THE END

ONE morning Lucy Alton wasn't very happy.

No, Lucy, you can't go into town with your friends. You know you promised to go and visit Mr Webster.

I didn't promise — Mum did! And I hate helping that old man! But, if I told them that, my friends wouldn't think much of me.

SECRETS

At Mr Webster's—

What a mess, Mr Webster!

I'm sorry, Lucy, but I was trying to sort out some old papers and became tired. If you just pile them up, I'll put them away in the case later.

However, Lucy opened the case.

35

You could have been killed! Don't you ever look where you're going?

S-sorry!

I thought someone called me — but there's no-one else here!

Lucy went home.

It was you, wasn't it, Cedric? You told me that my friends weren't worth bothering about because I've often thought that myself when I've been annoyed with them! I think, after all, I'd better take you back and put things right with Mr Webster!

But when Lucy returned to Mr Webster—

Mr Webster's still alseep, so I could just put Cedric back in the case. No . . . wait a moment! He's not asleep . . . he looks ill! I'd better call the doctor!

So, later—

The ambulance will take Mr Webster to hospital. You probably saved his life, young lady.

If that's true, it's the only nice thing I've done today — and, in a way, it's thanks to Cedric!

Then—

I'm going to have to apologise to everyone— but perhaps, now, you've made amends for spoiling Mr Webster's career, Cedric. I know what he was talking about now and I think it's better if you stay right here!

"Pity! Lucy and I made a good team! I wonder . . . who will be the next person to trust me with their secret thoughts?"

THE END

37

The Cautionary Tale Of Zenobia Babbitt

Zenobia — who's known as "Nobby"—
    Had a most unpleasant hobby.
When she was hardly out of bibs,
    She started telling dreadful fibs—
Nothing terribly malicious,
    Just ridiculously capricious.
"Nobby!" Her poor mum would cry.
    "It isn't ladylike to lie!
In fact, it makes you seem uncouth!
    You never speak a word of truth!"

But even smacks from Mrs Babbitt
    Couldn't stop her daughter's habit,
And, by the time she went to school,
    It had become the general rule
That every word Zenobia spoke
    Was quite untrue. "It's just a joke!"
She'd always plead. It wouldn't do—
    They all thought *that* was fibbing, too!

Eventually, her work in class
    Brought her to such a pretty pass,
That even if she really knew
    The answers to a test or two,
She'd find herself in quite a fix.
    Although she knew 1066
Was when the Normans England took,
    She couldn't write it in her book.
Instead, she found her straying pen
    Writing "It was 1910"!

In maths, as well, the situation
    Messed up her multiplication.
"Three times three is ten." She wept,
    Knowing it was quite inept.
When she brought home her school
    report
Her marks were all the same . . . yes,
    nought.

BED!

Her father thundered: "Off to bed!",
   Ashamed his girl was so ill-bred.
And Nobby, too, was close to tears.
   The marks had proved her deepest fears.
What started as a childish tease
   Had stuck with her; she couldn't cease.
And so, in a depression deep,
   Nobby cried herself to sleep.

And, as she slept, she had a dream . . .
   A fairy came upon the scene.
"Now, look here, Nobby," said the
   sprite,
"We're going to cure you . . . now,
   tonight.
I'm taking you to see a place
   Where fibbers go. You'll run apace
From dragons, goblins, demons, too.
   There'll be a test, just made for you.

"And if you pass, you can be free
   From all these horrid fibs, you see?"
So Nobby went, and saw a land
   Where monsters roamed, where flames
were fanned . . .
   She ran, and hid, quite terrified,
Until a castle she espied.
   A sign above its massive door
Read: "COME INSIDE AND FEAR NO
   MORE."

But how could she effect an entry?
   Two doors there were, each with a
sentry.
   "Ask a question," said a voice.
"Just one question, of your choice.
   One of those sentries, 'cross the way,
Is always truthful, come what may.
   The other one of evil reeks . . .
He tells a lie each time he speaks.
   Just one question, at one gate,
Will set you free — or seal your fate.
   One door leads to home, your base,
The other to the monsters' place.
   Make your choice without delay
Before the dragons come this way!"

So, gentle reader, if you will,
   Please help poor Nobby from this ill.
Now you know her awkward task,
   What is the question she must ask?
(There's not much time, so, if you're
   stuck
See page 40 — be in luck!)

The SOLUTION

There are a number of ways round this problem, but the simplest is probably this. Nobby walks up to one of the sentries and says: "Does the truthful sentry guard the door to freedom?"

1) If she is speaking to the truthful sentry, and he is standing in front of the door to freedom, he will say "yes".

2) If she is speaking to the lying sentry, and he is standing in front of the door to freedom, he will say "yes" (which is untrue, of course).

So whichever sentry she speaks to, if he answers "yes", then she goes through the door behind him. If he says "no", then she goes through the other door.

And you will learn, with great delight,
　That Nobby got the question right!
She woke next morning, sharp at
　eight,
Completely cured and feeling great.
　And nowadays, young Nobby's
known
　At school, in town, and back at
home,
　To everyone who passes by,
As, "She who never tells a lie"!

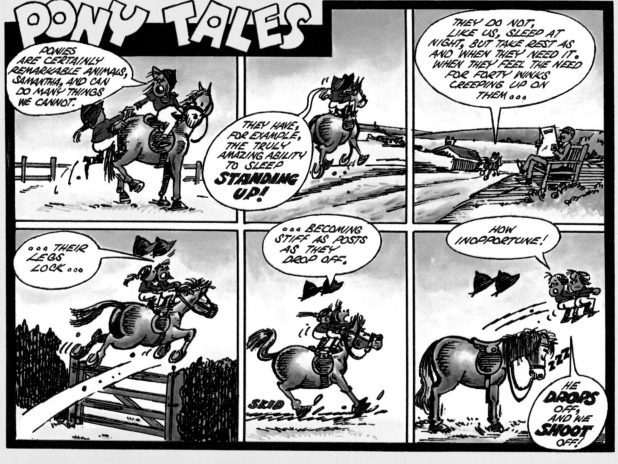

40

The Magic Typewriter

DOLLY MACHIN had never done well at school, as her teacher admitted to Dolly's parents.

Dolly's a likeable, kind, helpful and thoughtful girl . . . quite delightful, in fact. But her schoolwork is below standard.

I know she's always bottom of the class. Somehow, she just can't get her ideas together.

Every Saturday, Dolly ran errands for Miss Blandford, a retired headmistress.

Oh, thank you, Dolly, you're such a help. What's the matter?

Oh, just the usual — bottom of the class! Mum and Dad were getting on to me about it again.

Once inside—

Perhaps I can help. Would you like some extra coaching?

Thanks, Miss Blandford, but I'm afraid I'm just not bright enough. I can never remember things in exams.

Nonsense! You're very bright. You just can't organise your mind. I was like that at your age, yet I became a headmistress. I'll let you into the secret of how I did it. Come into the other room, Dolly.

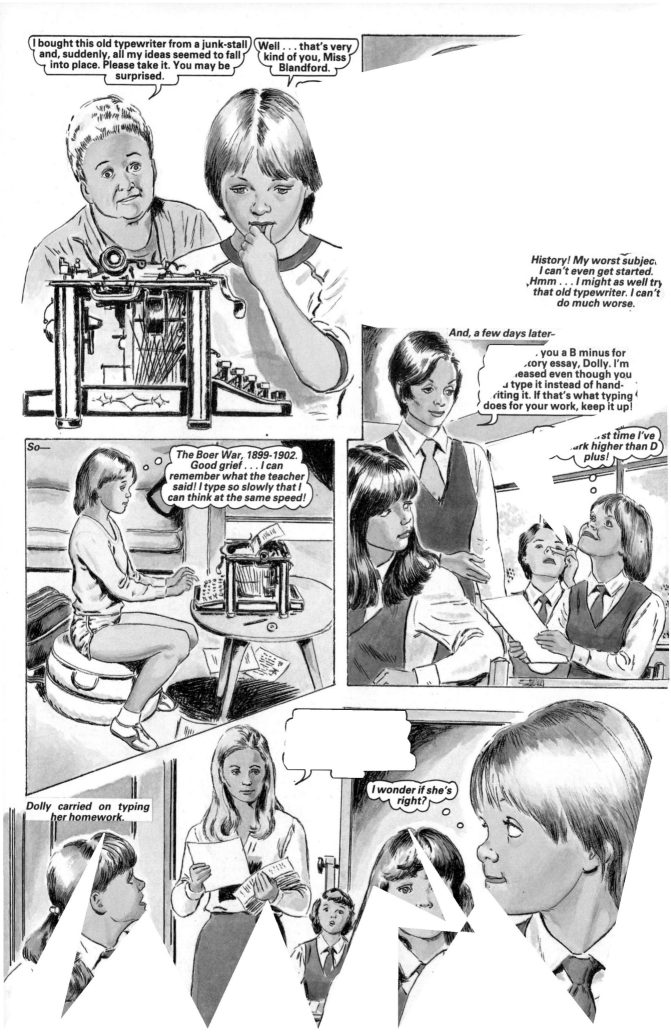

'Chaucer's position as the father of English Literature stems from the fact that I stole Dolly's typewriter. I stole Dolly's typewriter . . .' There's a page and a half, all the same.

But I . . . I didn't type . . . I mean, write . . . That typewriter! It's bewitched!

You'd better come with me to the headmaster, Sally.

Sally was suspended, and Dolly's typewriter was returned, but—

I'm afraid it's given its last gasp, Dolly. It's just not worth repairing.

I'll keep it anyway. I'm getting quite good marks now, and I'm sure it's all due to the typewriter.

Dolly told Miss Blandford all about it.

There was nothing magic about the typewriter, Dolly. It was within you to do well all the time. The machine just brought it out, that's all.

Well if it wasn't strange, how did it expose Sally — even after she copied her work by hand?

Because she had feelings of guilt. It was inside her, and the typewriter brought that out, too. Perhaps you're right, Dolly. Perhaps that's what real magic is. Now you can continue to do well thanks to the magic typewriter's help.

45

THE END

Wildlife

GAY and Andy Christie, who run a Wildlife Rescue Centre on their smallholding in North Ayrshire, look after lots of wild birds and animals every year.

Gay loves caring for the baby animals.

Vicki, the fox cub.

Hazel, the squirrel.

Lucy, the leveret.

Sammy, the roe deer fawn, was only three days old when he arrived.

Sammy became such good friends with Gay and Andy that, even after he had grown up and gone to live in the woods, he would come back for titbits and to go for walks with them. Gay spends a lot of time each day taking the young birds and animals into the woods and fields, so that they can learn how to find their own food and shelter.

46

Rescue Centre

Every spring and summer, lots of young birds fall out of their nests, so Gay keeps a varied collection of baskets that make good homes for birds like these baby swallows or this fluffy young kestrel.

Vicki, the fox cub, was brought to the Rescue Centre after her mother had been killed by dogs. Though frightened at first, she soon made friends with Gay and her Alsatian, Tish.

Many of the birds Gay and Andy look after have been hit by cars. This kestrel had a broken wing, but she was naughty and kept trying to pick the plaster off with her strong, hooked beak. She had to be kept in an old sock until her wing had healed.

Rumpus, the otter, is Gay's favourite animal. Every day, after breakfast, he wanders off on his own, but he is always home in time for tea. If he is tired, he cuddles up with his favourite dog, Tangle.

Usually he wants to play. His favourite toys are his football and brush.

Rumpus likes to help Gay and Andy around the house, but Gay says it's difficult to wash the dishes with Rumpus swimming in the sink!

47

HOLLANDEN
SURVIVAL CENTRE FOR RARE FARM ANIMALS

PETS' CORNER

PORTLAND SHEEP

ERISKAY PONY

A centre to protect endangered farm animals has been opened to the public at Great Hollanden Farm, Hildenborough, near Sevenoaks, Kent. The collection, brought together by fruit farmer Brian Brooks, features more than a hundred animals, including particularly rare species of ponies, cattle, sheep and pigs. All the animals at the survival centre were once common, but progressively intensive industrial farming methods have largely eliminated these breeds and many have become almost extinct.

Among the most spectacular animals at Hollanden is the Portland sheep. Legend has it that these animals swam ashore from the sinking ships of the Spanish Armada in 1588. During the following 200 years, they became one of the nation's most prolific sheep breeds. By the 18th century, though, their numbers dramatically declined until now they are Britain's rarest sheep.

One of the major attractions of the collection are the four Eriskay ponies. From the Scottish island of Eriskay, they make up about 10 per cent of the breed's entire population. Two of them were saved from a Glasgow knacker's yard, while the other pair were brought straight from the island.

Here are some of the rare animals at the farm.

WHITE PARK CATTLE

JACOB'S SHEEP

WEST HIGHLAND COW AND CALF

BAGOT GOATS

49

50

CHRISTMAS VIDEO

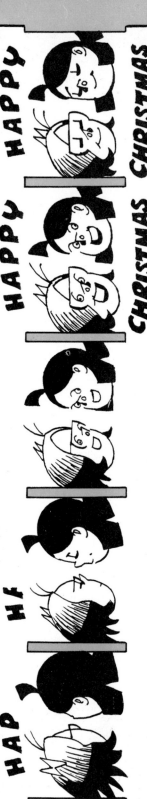

THE FIRST EVER VIDEO GREETINGS CARD FROM **US** TO **YOU!**

TAPE

WHOOPEE! SEE US COME TO LIFE, RIGHT THERE IN YOUR ROOM! CUT OUT THE TWO PIC STRIPS — OR TRACE OFF, TO AVOID CUTTING YOUR ANNUAL, AND PASTE TO A PIECE OF THIN CARD 15 CM. WIDE AND THE LENGTH OF THE STRIPS, AS ABOVE, WITH A SHARP KNIFE (MIND YOUR FINGERS!), AND A STRAIGHT-EDGE, CAREFULLY CUT OUT THE SLOTS BETWEEN THE PICS. PAINT THE BACK OF THE PICS BLACK (SEE BELOW). BEND ROUND INTO A CYLINDER WITH THE PICS ON THE INSIDE, FASTENING WITH STICKY TAPE.

JUST PUT IT ON YOUR RECORD PLAYER AND VIEW THROUGH THE SLOTS AS DEB IS DOING BELOW.

IT'S SUPER **FUN**-TASTIC!

First-Time Faith

FAITH HOPE wanted to be the girl with the most entries in a local firm's Book of Records, so she spent her time thinking up things that had never been done, then doing them — much to the amusement of her friends.

I want to be the first person in Bilsea to dig up the remains of a Roman villa. I'll not only make the Book of Records, I'll go down in local history. Perhaps I'll even be an archaeologist when I leave school, instead of an astronaut.

Yes, well, just hang on a minute, Faith. Where are you going to find this Roman villa?

Faith already had found it.

Clever dog, Patch! And I thought you were digging up a bone! This is going to make us both famous!

Patch uncovered part of a really old paved floor, and there are Roman numerals carved into it. It's on Mr Higgs' land — that field behind the cowsheds.

The kindly farmer had agreed to let Faith start digging.

Just don't play anywhere I've got stuff growing, young Faith.

Thanks, Mr Higgs.

Play? Little does he know I'm engaged on serious research excavation!

Faith's friends showed interest.

I've always fancied doing a dig.

So have I. Tell you what, Faith — we'll help you. When do we start?

You don't start! I'm the one who wants to make the Book of Records, so I've got to do this alone!

And so —

I didn't expect the digging to be so hard, but it'll . . . puff . . . be worth it . . . puff . . . when I see my name in the Book of Records.

Just then — Hey! Faith! What do you think you're up to?

It's all right, Willie, I've got permission from your dad.

I've found a Roman villa! Look at this! These are Roman numerals, Willie. Perhaps the date the house was built, or something like that. It's an important find. What's so funny?

Ha! Ha! Ha! Heh! Heh! Heh!

Nothing at all, Faith. Er . . . you just keep digging. I'm off for a cool lemonade.

Boy, that Willie Higgs is a dope! If he weren't such a bumpkin, he'd have offered to bring me back a cold lemonade and a cheese roll!

Willie returned about an hour later, bringing some friends with him.

How are you getting on, Faith? Found Cleopatra's Needle yet?

You dope! Cleopatra wasn't Roman!

Another half hour went slowly by.

Nothing so far. I can't understand it. I'd expected to uncover at least some Roman coins by now. I'll just have to dig deeper.

You look exhausted, Faith. Have you seen my boy Willie?

Phew! Willie was here, Mr Higgs, but he went off somewhere with his pals.

Oh, he did, did he? Well, I told him to dig up this patch so I could plant my lettuces this afternoon. How did he con you into it?

Lettuces? Is that why he came here?

Mr Higgs, you said I could dig up this old Roman villa, and that's what I've been doing.

Old Roman villa? On my land? What are you talking about?

See those Roman numerals? I imagine it's the date the villa was built — probably for some rich......

Heh! Heh! Heh! Give me the spade! Heh! Heh!

BOBBY DAZZLER

ROBERTA DAZZLER, known as Bobby to her friends, was the only girl at Westbury School for Boys, where her mother was the matron. Bobby claimed that anything the boys could do, she could do better.

Look at that! A year ago Roy Wesley was here at Westbury, swotting over his homework! And look at him now — getting into the big time!

He was never much interested in music, was he, Mike? Always tinkering with electronic stuff.

EX-SCHOOLBOY IN THE CHARTS

Mike's enthusiasm was fired, of course.

We've not played together for ages, Mike.

Oh, we'll soon get back into practice. If Roy Wesley can get into the charts, so can we!

I'll be lead singer, if you like.

Better not — Bobby's too good a singer. She'd show us up.

Er, no thanks, Bobby. This is an all-boys' band.

Huh! All noise, more like!

What's the tape-recorder for, Mike?

When we've practised a bit, we'll do a demo tape and send it to Roy Wesley.

But there was no need. The following week—

Have you heard the news? Roy Wesley — he's come back on a visit!

Great! We'll ask him to listen to our band — but not a word to Bobby, right?

Bobby had already met Roy.

I don't remember you being a singer at school, Roy.

Oh, it's one of those talents I never developed until after I left, Bobby. Is the grub still good at the tuck-shop?

Hey! What does he think he's doing taking my girlfriend into the tuck-shop?

Steady, Mike! Punching him in the nose isn't going to get him to listen to our tape! Besides, he's bigger than you!

Young Wesley called in to see me this afternoon. I don't recall his having any musical talent when he was at school.

If you'd heard his record, Headmaster, you'd realise that very little has changed!

Finally, Mike managed to speak to Roy, alone.

Hi, Roy...remember me? Mike Norton? I — we've — got a bit of a band together and I wondered if you'd listen to us.

Oh? Yes, well, I suppose I could fit you in. I'm pretty busy. Friday afternoon? What did you say your name was?

What a big-headed creep!

Shut up, Freddy! We can be nice to him until Friday, can't we?

Roy invited Bobby to stay with his family at the weekend.

The school's having a free weekend, anyway. My dad can show you round the recording studio.

I didn't realise your father owned the recording company, Roy. I'd love to see how records are really made.

On Friday—

Quick! Bobby's coming! We mustn't let her know that Roy's auditioning us in half an hour! Outside!

But she's bound to be suspicious, Mike!

Mike! Where are you off to in such a hurry?

Er, there's a football practice in half an hour. See you, Bobby.

Moments later—

I just saw Mike Norton and the boys. Where were they off to?

Football practice, they said. I thought they were going to play for you, like you said.

So did I, but if they're not bothered, I'm not. If we hurry, we can catch the five o'clock train.

All right, Roy. I'll go and get my things together.

An hour later—

What can have happened to Roy? He was supposed to be here at five!

Roy Wesley? He's gone. I overheard Bobby telling him you'd gone to football practice, so they left straight away.

This is all your fault, Mike! You and your bright ideas!

Well, how was I to know? Never mind...we can still send him the tape!

We can't — it's gone! The music department must have taken it back!

58

The Story of FURNIVAL

This is the story of Furnival Fly,
Who met a thin grass snake and couldn't get by.
He pushed and he grunted to try to squeeze past.
"No *good!*" hissed the snake. "We are both wedged too fast!"

Then Furnival knew he had grown much too stout
And would have to do something to thin himself out.
But how to get moving? And what could he say?
Gasped the snake: "Here comes someone who'll pull me away!"

It was Montague Mouse, and he stared at the sight
Of Furnival straining with all of his might.
"Pull my tail!" said the snake. "And don't mind if I cry—
I must get away from this overweight fly!"

The mouse rolled his sleeves up and tried to feel strong.
He tugged at the snake, who became twice as long.
But it made him much thinner, so Furnival squeezed
And bounced himself forward — my word, was he pleased!

The snake slid off quickly between the grass banks.
"I like *that!*" cried Monty. "He never said thanks!"
Furnival, gasping, had picked up his hat,
And was wondering aloud how to get down his fat.

"Jogging's the answer," said Montague Mouse.
"Though I get all *my* exercise cleaning the house."
So Furnival tried it, but set such a pace
That he crawled home all sticky and red in the face.

'You ought to try rowing. I'll lend you my boat,"
Said Harrington Harvey, a handsome young stoat.
But Furnival's weight made the boat go around,
And he lost both the oars — oh, how Harrington frowned!

"We'll cycle to Frink — I can find you a bike,"
Said Montague Mouse. "Bring some lunch, if you like."
So Furnival cooked an enormous meat pie,
Which made him much fatter — the silly young fly.

The way home seemed longer. The hill was so steep
That Furnival wished he could lie down and sleep.
He pedalled and puffed, but the bike just stood still,
Then it slowly rolled back to the foot of the hill.

"It's no good," thought Furnival, feeling upset.
"The harder I'm trying, the bigger I get.
But what I must do, if I get any fatter,
Is find the right job where my size doesn't matter."

So now, when the circus comes into *your* town,
Go and see the fine fellow dressed up as a clown.
He's clever and funny — you'll laugh till you cry.
Who is it? You've guessed — it's big Furnival Fly.

DANGER
MIN at WORK

They want someone to sell admission tickets. That should be easy.

WHEN Min left school, her hardest job was keeping a job. One day, Min had been given a job in a castle museum.

There's armour, old weapons . . . all good solid stuff that's lasted hundreds of years. But we know your reputation, so keep out of here!

What's this iron cage for?

Criminals were put into that and hung from the top of the gate.

But, your job is in the ticket office so, don't let me find you anywhere else.

Er . . . yes . . .

There's not much elbow room in here, especially if I get busy! GRRR! Now the door's stuck! Perhaps if I give it a good hard thump...

Which Min did!

Oops!

As the ticket-box fell over, it knocked the drawbridge handle.

WOOSH!

SLAM!

Help!

Min felt let down—and so was the drawbridge!

Min got out just in time.

Phew! That was close!

I'll just pop up here and have a look at how the drawbridge works.

62

FIRST MAKE THE BODY, USING THICKISH MATERIAL, CUTTING OUT THE LARGER SHAPE SHOWN RIGHT IN BOTH BLACK AND WHITE. PUT THESE RIGHT SIDES TOGETHER, SEW ROUND EXCEPT AT THE BOTTOM, THEN TURN RIGHT SIDES OUT, FINISHING AS AT PIC 1 BELOW. TURN THE BOTTOM IN AND GLUE.

DO EXACTLY THE SAME FOR THE FLIPPERS, CUTTING TWO WHITE PIECES, TWO BLACK, THEN TREATING THE SAME AS THE BODY. GLUE THESE IN PLACE 10 CM. FROM THE TOP OF THE HEAD, AS IN THE BIG PIC.

THE BEAK PATTERN IS GIVEN FULL-SIZE LEFT. CUT OUT IN STOUT CARD FROM THE BEAK POINT DOWN TO THE DOTTED LINE. CUT THE SAME SHAPE IN WHITE MATERIAL AND GLUE THE TWO TOGETHER AS IN PIC 2.

BEND THE END DOWN TO THE ASTERISK AS SHOWN IN 3. NOW CUT THE WHOLE OF THE BEAK SHAPE OUT IN BLACK AND GLUE TO THE CARD PIECE AS SHOWN IN 3 AND 4.

GLUE THIS TO THE HEAD AS SHOWN IN THE BIG PIC, THEN GLUE ON ROUND, BLACK EYES. STUFF THE HEAD WITH A BALL OF NEWSPRINT GLUED INTO PLACE, AND HE'S COMPLETED.

Handy Tips

to make life easier.

Here are some tips that will make your life that little bit easier.

SAUCE BOTTLE DREGS

How often have you tried, in vain, to knock out what's left at the bottom of a sauce or ketchup bottle? Here's the answer to the problem. Hold the bottom of the bottle so that the top, with the lid tightly shut, is pointing towards the ground. Then, making sure that you have plenty of room, whirl your arm round and round like a propeller. This will move the remaining sauce from the bottom to the top of the bottle. Now, you can easily get it out.

KEEPING DRINKS FIZZY

If you don't want to finish all your fizzy drink from a metal-topped bottle, pour what you want into a glass, then drop the handle of a teaspoon down the neck of the newly-opened bottle. The remainder in the bottle will remain reasonably fizzy for quite a few hours. This works with most fizzy drinks.

BUTTON SEWING

Sometimes a button is pulled off, taking a whole piece of cloth with it. It's not impossible to sew it back on in the same place without patching! Simply sew the button in the centre of a piece of strong, straight tape, then push the button through the hole in the garment from the back. Position it correctly then sew the tape firmly in place on the inside. A job well done!

STORING SHOES

I expect you all have problems keeping your shoes tidy. Here's a handy tip for keeping them organised. Collect old shoe boxes, cut one end off each box, then stack them at the bottom of your clothes cupboard with the ends facing you. Use the little compartments, and your shoes can be slid in and out easily.

STICKY ANSWER

Most of you probably stick posters on your bedroom walls with Blu-Tack, or similar substances. But what do you do when you want to change your wall decorations around? If the sticky stuff is fresh and soft, it will come off the wall cleanly. If a small bit remains, dab it with a larger lump. However, if it's dried, this may not work. The way to remove it then, is simply to rub it gently with the sticky side of a piece of masking tape. Your mum and dad will be pleased!

ROSE GREEN, an only child, was not happy when her parents decided to adopt another girl of her own age.

"WE DO!"

But why, Mum? I like being on my own, I keep telling you!

Darling, your father and I have never liked the idea of single child families.

You'll soon get used to the idea, Rose. Before long, you'll wonder how you ever lived without a sister.

Sister? I haven't got a sister, and I don't want one!

A girl brought up in a Children's Home! I bet she'll be rowdy and interfere with my things . . . especially with my books.

The thing Rose liked best in the world was to read.

I think I'll take my new Alice Awkright story down to the meadow and try to forget that this awful girl is arriving today.

Rose had made up her mind that she wouldn't like her new sister.

This is probably the last time I'll be able to come down here and read in peace. She'll be following me about, chattering and giggling.

Alice Awkright was her favourite heroine of fiction. Rose shared all her adventures.

Oh! This is awful! Alice's parents have been killed! She's an orphan . . . and without any money!

70

As usual, though now in a Children's Home, Alice faced her fate bravely . . .

I-I'll soon be adopted. I'll go and live with some loving family. There'll be other boys and girls... my new brothers and sisters. I-I'll have a home again.

Don't depend on it, Alice. Most people prefer to adopt babies.

No-one wants to take on a big girl of eleven. You must make up your mind that this is your home now.

It's not that I'm not grateful. Everyone's very kind here. But-but doing everything by bells. . . sleeping fifteen to a dormitory . . .

Nowhere private to keep my special treasures . . . never being alone. But I must bear it . . . I must . . . if nobody wants me.

The story was a bit too near the truth for Rose.

I-I don't think I'll read any more at the moment. The sun's making me feel a bit drowsy. I think I'll take a nap.

Rose couldn't get away from Alice, even in her dreams.

Another baby adopted. . . that's three this week. Oh, if only some family would take me — but I'm too old to be adopted.

Alice — please don't cry! Try to be brave as you always are!

Remember in "The Secret of Castle Gary"?

I had a family then. . . I had a home. Oh, Rose, I've tried so hard to be brave, but I feel so alone!

71

If I had you for a sister, Rose. . . if we could share our secrets, laugh over things, grow up together . . .

Rose awoke gradually, still speaking to Alice.

Don't worry, Alice. All your books have happy endings, and I'm sure this one will.

Why, I-I've been dreaming! And what a dream! It was so real — just as if I were living it!

The dream had made a lot of things clear to Rose.

I've been mean to this girl Mum and Dad have adopted. She must have felt the way Alice did in my dream . . . wanting a home and a family, crying when no-one was near.

And I've been so selfish. It took Alice to show me how wrong I was.

Mum, I've changed my mind. It's not right that I should have so much and Alice — I mean, some other girls — so little. I'm glad you're adopting this girl.

Darling, I'm so glad!

I want to make her feel really at home from the start. So tell me all about her ... her name ... where she comes from.

There's no need, Rose. She can tell you herself.

She's upstairs. We weren't expecting her until tonight, but she arrived ten minutes ago.

I'll go straight up to her, then.

Odd! She arrived just as I was dreaming of Alice!

Rose entered the girl's room a little nervously.

Hello . . . I'm Rose, your new sister.

Hello, Rose. I'm Alison.

It-it's the girl in my dream! The same sweet face . . . the same long, blonde hair!

It was just like hearing Alice speak in her dream.

I'm so glad to be here, Rose. I was made an orphan last year. My parents were killed in an accident, and I've been so lonely.

I thought I'd find another family soon. I waited and waited . . . went on hoping . . . but everybody wants babies. Nobody wants a big girl of eleven.

We do, Alison! We do!

THE END

73

Sir Gallivant

SIR GALLIVANT, noble knight and rescuer of damsels in distress, was bored with life in days of old.

This ring was given to me by an Arabian princess I rescued from a dragon.

Think you so? Then I shall try it.

Odds bodkins! What is happening?

Verily, it looks right magical. Try rubbing it, sire.

What is your command, o master?

Eh? What? Er — pray transport me one thousand years hence. I often wonder what it will be like in the future.

Thy wish is my command!

Sir Gallivant found himself in a present-day street — in the rush hour.

Gadzooks! Metal monsters!

Sir Gallivant clanked down the road and came to a school crossing.

Egad! A ga... ...ss! I must rescue her!

74

Impressed, the manager picked up the telephone.

Er — accommodation, did you say, sir? My brother runs a first-class hotel near here.

Hotel Moderne? That you, Sid? I've got a rum customer here! Can you put him up? He's loaded!

What magic is this? Methinks he hears his brother through an ear trumpet!

Soon—

HOTEL MODER

Welcome to the Hotel Moderne, sir! I will personally show you to your room.

What a wondrous castle! How magical is this 20th Century!

FANCY DRESS TO-NIGHT

In the lift—

Just press this button, and up we go.

Methinks my stomach is left behind!

In the hotel bedroom—

Hot or cold water at the turn of a tap.

This is the light switch.

And this is the telephone to call for room service.

Gadzooks! 'Tis witchcraft!

The manager left to supervise the fancy-dress dance.

Methinks I should like to see this fancy dress affair.

Somehow, Sir Gallivant reached the ballroom, but—

BLA BOOM! SHRIEK BOOM

Odds bodkins! These varlets and wenches seem to be going mad!

The terrible noise hurts my head! I must flee!

But the lift was stuck!

Trapped! Like an animal in a cage! I must summon the genie!

So—

What is your wish, o master?

Get me out of here! I would return to the days of no cars, no supermarkets, no credit cards and no lifts! Give me a nice, simple, fire-breathing dragon to contend with, and I'll be happy!

The End

COMMUNITY NURSE

CAROL HARVEY was employed by Davenport and District Health Centre as a community nurse. Carol treated patients in their own homes and enjoyed her work. One afternoon, Carol called at the home of nine-year-old Alison Ford, who had lost the use of her legs as a result of a road accident.

Hello, Nurse Carol. These are for you. I know you like flowers, and I remembered you said you live in a flat and haven't got a garden.

That's right — just a window-box. Thank you very much, Alison. Roses are my favourites.

When you've massaged my legs, Terry's going to take me to the park. I am lucky to have a brother like Terry.

Good idea.

Yes, he's a good lad. Never minds giving up his time to Alison. Thinks the world of her.

After the treatment, Carol went to have a chat with Mrs Ford.

Have you and your husband reached a decision yet about the operation, Mrs Ford?

Well, my worry is, if it failed, would Alison be worse off . . . perhaps unable even to sit up?

There's no danger of that, Mrs Ford. It is a comparatively new technique, but Mr Roberts has had a high success rate. He is a very fine surgeon.

You are right, Nurse. Alison mustn't be denied this chance of freedom from the wheelchair.

Two days later —

RECEPTION

X-RAY

RECO

Carol, Mrs Ford telephoned while you were at lunch. She'd like you to call in on her this afternoon. She sounded very upset.

Can she have changed her mind about the operation?

Thank goodness you've come! Alison's in ever such a state, Nurse. She says she's scared of going into hospital.

Oh, dear!

Here I am, Alison. I came as quickly as I could.

Nurse Carol! I'm scared! I'm scared!

78

There's no need to be frightened, Simon. I know, you see, because I was there for two months after my accident, and then twice again for operations.

Nurse Carol will have tried to reassure him, but perhaps he'd take more notice of me.

Fingers crossed!

No. You won't mind it, Simon. If you like, I'll tell you what happens.

Yes, please.

Phew! I think it's going to be all right! Alison is concerned for Simon, just as I hoped.

Later —

It's a very nice tea, but I don't get very hungry.

You should eat well, Simon, to make you strong and ready for your operation. I don't feel all that hungry, but I'm going to try to clear my plate.

Alison looks, and sounds, calmer.

When it was time for Carol and Simon to leave —

You know something, Nurse Carol? Talking to Simon, trying to reassure him, has somehow reassured me. Well, I'm still a bit afraid, but not nearly so much.

That's good news, Alison. See you tomorrow. And thank you for helping Simon.

Caring about Simon took her mind off herself and her own fears, just as I hoped. She hadn't lost her courage — just mislaid it.

Six weeks later —

Sister said I could walk along the corridor to meet you! I'm to go home tomorrow, and soon I won't need this stick! Mr Roberts says that before very long, I'll be able to run!

That's wonderful news, Alison! I am very, very happy for you!

THE END

79

MOIRA and her friends had been in town all day to spend their Christmas money.

The sale at the Co-op doesn't start until tomorrow, so why don't you 'phone your mum and ask her if you can stay with me tonight? That way, we can get here as soon as the shop opens in the morning.

OK — but if Mum says 'no', I'll have to go home soon. The bus to our estate only runs every hour.

Moira's Midnight BARGAINS!

Aileen and June are waiting for me in the café on the top floor of the Co-op. These people have been chatting for ages — my friends will be wondering what's keeping me!

Meanwhile, in the café—

Sorry, girls, but the café's closing now. If you hurry, you'll catch the last lift down. It's a long trudge by the stairs!

Oh!

Moira's mother must have said 'no' and she's gone for her bus.

It was no use.

Every door is locked! Mum thinks I'm staying with June, and June must think I've gone home! Nobody will realise I'm trapped inside the store!

Moira decided to make the best of it.

Well, at least I can look at tomorrow's bargains. Mum would love this ornament and I could just about afford it.

And I don't think I'm too old to have this cute soft toy sitting at the bottom of my bed!

And, in the sports department—

This is fun — but I'm getting hungry.

Luckily, the store had a grocery hall.

Well, at least I'm not going to starve to death!

I'll leave the money by the till. If there was anyone here, they'd have seen me on the security cameras. The place must be totally deserted.

Now to enjoy my meal and read this book I picked up in the book department. And I might as well have the radio on for company.

But, after a while—

And now, listeners, it's time to 'phone in with your problems. Perhaps we can sort them out for you . . .

Oh, this book is scary! 'Phone? Why didn't I think of that? There must be a 'phone in the building somewhere . . . perhaps in the offices on the top floor.

Moira was out of luck.

All the doors are locked — perhaps I'd better find somewhere comfortable to sleep. I wish I hadn't read those ghost stories!

But, when she got back—

My food . . . the book . . . the radio... everything's gone! Th-that means I'm not alone in the store!

Moira ran fearfully through the store.

P-Perhaps there's a ghost! B-but would a ghost take biscuits?

Suddenly—

AAAAAH!

PEPPER the PONY

"LET'S GET TOGETHER!"

JULIE CARTER was known as The Brain of Beesdale—and, frankly, it bored her silly.

Hey, Julie, you've been voted the girl likely to get the most "A" levels in the school's history!

Groovy . . . I don't think!

What's the matter? Don't you like being the brainiest girl in the school?

I love it. But why couldn't I fall for the brainiest *boy* in the school?

Who, Specs Johnson? His idea of a romantic evening is a walk round the Science Museum!

I know! Peg — what do you reckon Bill Mason's idea of a romantic evening is?

Bill Mason! Oh, no — don't tell me you've gone and fallen for *him!*

Well, I have. And he's not the studious type. On the other hand, he's the greatest Captain of Games Beesdale's ever had.

And, Peg — brains and games just don't mix. Bill Mason has never even noticed I'm alive.

As it happened, Bill had noticed Julie — more than once.

Bill, why are you always glancing over at that drippy Julie Carter?

I don't think she's drippy, Marie. Just a bit on the quiet side.

He is interested in her! You'd better put a stop to that, Marie, my girl!

No, you're right . . . she isn't really a drip. Her trouble is, she despises boys who are what she calls all brawn and no brain. Aggie could tell you.

Did she really say that, Aggie?

Aggie caught on to Marie's plan quickly.

Oh, she's always felt like that. She dated my brother and spent the whole evening sneering at him because of his low marks in maths.

That's my worst subject! Yours, too, isn't it, Bill?

Marie was leaving nothing to chance. In the girls' cloakroom that evening—

Wasn't Bill funny last night about brainy girls? Romance busters, he called them! Ha! Ha!

Said an evening with one of them was like sitting your "O" levels all over again! He's a scream!

But Marie's scheme wasn't working out the way she hoped.

Funny — Julie seems far too nice a girl to make fun of someone for getting low marks.

I'll help you. Look, you just slide this ladder along. The book you want is the third from the left — the blue one.

Thanks a lot, Julie. Er — mind if I sit by you while I'm studying in case I need any more help?

So— You see, Cromwell's ideas were very puritan, and they made him bigoted and cruel.

I get it. Hey, this is fascinating stuff! I had no idea!

Julie was being picked up by her father.

'Bye, Bill. Er — see you at the library again sometime.

Sure, Julie. 'Bye for now.

But I've had enough of Cromwellian England to last me a month. What I need now is a good work-out.

Later, at the local gym—

Hello, Joe, is the apparatus free? Thought I'd do a spell on the rowing machine, followed by a session on the parallel bars . . .

Leave the rowing machine till last, Bill. One of your school mates is on it.

First time she's even *seen* one, if you ask me. Getting into a right mess, she is.

JULIE!

THE END

CATCALL

CATNIP

OUCH!

CATALOGUE

CATASTROPHE

1st PRIZE

CATERPILLAR

Brother

CATALYST

Auntie

Pussy Willows

CATKIN

CATACOMB

CATARRH

CATERWAUL

CATATONIC

Judy Nature Calendar 1987

January

Su. ..		4	11	18	25
M. ..		5	12	19	26
Tu. ..		6	13	20	27
W. ..		7	14	21	28
Th. ..	1	8	15	22	29
F. ..	2	9	16	23	30
S. ..	3	10	17	24	31

FEEDING TIME FOR A LAMB . . .

. . . AND FOR BABY ROBINS

February

Su. ..	1	8	15	22
M. ..	2	9	16	23
Tu. ..	3	10	17	24
W. ..	4	11	18	25
Th. ..	5	12	19	26
F. ..	6	13	20	27
S. ..	7	14	21	28

March

Su. ..	1	8	15	22	29
M. ..	2	9	16	23	30
Tu. ..	3	10	17	24	31
W. ..	4	11	18	25	
Th. ..	5	12	19	26	
F. ..	6	13	20	27	
S. ..	7	14	21	28	

MUTE SWANS

Judy Nature Calendar 1987

April

Su.	..		5	12	19	26
M.	..		6	13	20	27
Tu.	..		7	14	21	28
W.	..	1	8	15	22	29
Th.	..	2	9	16	23	30
F.	..	3	10	17	24	
S.	..	4	11	18	25	

GANNET

May

Su.	..		3	10	17	24/31
M.	..		4	11	18	25
Tu.	..		5	12	19	26
W.	..		6	13	20	27
Th.	..		7	14	21	28
F.	..	1	8	15	22	29
S.	..	2	9	16	23	30

June

Su.	..		7	14	21	28
M.	..	1	8	15	22	29
Tu.	..	2	9	16	23	30
W.	..	3	10	17	24	
Th.	..	4	11	18	25	
F.	..	5	12	19	26	
S.	..	6	13	20	27	

Judy Nature Calendar 1987

July

Su.	..		5	12	19 26
M.	..		6	13	20 27
Tu.	..		7	14	21 28
W.	..	1	8	15	22 29
Th.	..	2	9	16	23 30
F.	..	3	10	17	24 31
S.	..	4	11	18	25

OYSTER CATCHER

FUNGI

August

Su.	..		2	9	16	23/30
M.	..		3	10	17	24/31
Tu.	..		4	11	18	25
W.	..		5	12	19	26
Th.	..		6	13	20	27
F.	..		7	14	21	28
S.	..	1	8	15	22	29

September

Su.	..		6	13	20 27
M.	..		7	14	21 28
Tu.	..	1	8	15	22 29
W.	..	2	9	16	23 30
Th.	..	3	10	17	24
F.	..	4	11	18	25
S.	..	5	12	19	26

RED FOX

Judy
Nature
Calendar
1987

October

Su.	..		4	11	18 25
M.	..		5	12	19 26
Tu.	..		6	13	20 27
W.	..		7	14	21 28
Th.	..	1	8	15	22 29
F.	..	2	9	16	23 30
S.	..	3	10	17	24 31

November

Su.	..	1	8	15	22 29
M.	..	2	9	16	23 30
Tu.	..	3	10	17	24
W.	..	4	11	18	25
Th.	..	5	12	19	26
F.	..	6	13	20	27
S.	..	7	14	21	28

December

Su.	..		6	13	20 27
M.	..		7	14	21 28
Tu.	..	1	8	15	22 29
W.	..	2	9	16	23 30
Th.	..	3	10	17	24 31
F.	..	4	11	18	25
S.	..	5	12	19	26

GREYLAG

IN SEARCH of ORYANA

IN the sky above Peru, Dr Armand Sanches, a famous archaeologist, and his daughter, Margarita, were on an expedition to the legendary city of Tihuanaco.

The local Indians say the ancient city of Tihuanaco was built for a goddess who came out of the sky. She had four fingers, and was supposed to be the "mother of humanity". They called her Oryana, and built a temple to her at Tihuanaco.

And what do you think, Dad?

There's a theory that the goddess was really a visitor from space, who strayed onto the Earth in primitive times.

Do you really believe that, Dad?

That's what we're going to find out. Look, there's the plateau of Tihuanaco over there.

Suddenly —

What's happening? I can't control the plane! Call the airfield in Cuzco!

I can't! The radio's gone dead! We're going to crash!

Margarita was knocked unconscious in the crash. When she regained her senses —

Aaaaah!

Ow, my hand! I must have broken my thumb! What is this place? I don't remember seeing a river. This plain has been arid for centuries. And where's the plane? Where's Dad?

The settlement at Tihuanaco can't be far away. I must get there and radio for help. I . . . I must . . .

But the heat, and exhaustion, caused Margarita to collapse again. When she awoke —

Oh . . . what's happened? Who are you?

I wife of Amahatl. You rest.

Later —

I, Amahatl, chief of Nazca people, find you as if dead. Bring here.

I know the Indian dialects, but this one is so ancient! And those clothes . . . the old Inca dress! It's almost as if I had gone back in time!

Is that the temple of Tihuanaco? Are you repairing it?

Repair? What is repair? We are building temple, to glory of Quetzalcoatl. It is work of many years. Almost finished now.

It can't be Tihuanaco, then, because that was built centuries ago. We must have gone off-course. How am I going to get back to Cuzco?

Unable to leave the village, Margarita busied herself looking after the needs of the natives, with the aid of herbs gathered from nearby. The months slipped by, and the people came to regard her as some sort of superior being, who could heal all ills. They began to call her "Mother" as she supervised the well-being of the Nazca children. Then, one day, the chief came to see her.

The temple is finished. Tomorrow our people will go to give thanks to the gods who sent you to help us. You will mount the temple steps with me.

Next day —

I don't understand! It looks just like the pictures of the temple of Tihuanaco, but these people have just finished building it!

This day we thank the gods for sending us help in the form of our Mother. This temple shall be known as Tihuanaco, in honour of her coming.

But, that's not right! The temple was dedicated to the Earth-Mother, Oryana, the four-fingered goddess!

So be it!

My broken thumb — caused by the crash! They think I've only got four fingers! But they can't confuse me with an ancient goddess!

As the crowd cheered, Margarita realised what had happened.

Here is our four-fingered Mother Goddess, who came from the sky!

I must somehow have slipped back all those centuries! And that must mean that the woman who came down from the sky is me! I am Oryana!

HAIL, ORYANA!

THE END

Samantha

SAMANTHA knew deep down that she shouldn't have left the house, but she couldn't resist it. It wasn't that she hated home; just that she felt that there should be more to life than dull routine. There was no adventure. Let's face it — she felt imprisoned in her own home.

Hurrying along the High Street as the rain pelted down, Samantha began to regret her impulsive action. She was cold and damp. Her nose was almost quivering as the water, dripping off the end of it, made her face look shiny.

However, as the sky darkened, Samantha's confidence returned. No longer was she going to be just the little one of the family. She was free.

Looking around her, Samantha felt a little lost. She remembered passing the vet's at the very bottom of the High Street — but where was she now? Should she turn back? No, she couldn't face the disapproval of everybody at home.

Samantha hadn't even thought about her future as she made her quick getaway. She hadn't brought one scrap of food or anything else with her, and now she realised how silly she had been to leave her favourite possessions scattered about her room. She thought longingly of the special, large mirror she had been given. Samantha did not think she was vain, but she could have gazed in that mirror for hours. Then she remembered her exerciser, set up in a corner of her room for her nightly keep-fit class.

At last Samantha came to a park on the outskirts of town, which she clearly remembered from being tiny. She thought of

the days later, when she had gone with the others to watch them play on the swings. She had been too scared to join in that, but she did love going down the slide because it was just like her one at home except on a bigger scale.

The memories upset Samantha more. Feeling miserable, she sat on a well-worn park bench, trying to block out her thoughts. She was hungry now. She couldn't even remember when she had last eaten — but where now was she to find food? She reckoned that it was about 11.00 pm and not many shops are open at that time in Eastbourne. In any case, Samantha was very fussy about her food.

Wandering over to a part of the park covered in enormous elm trees, all she could see was a discarded jam doughnut. It was absolutely disgusting and covered in grass.

Suddenly she sensed something close by her. Slowly looking round, she faced beside her the most enormous dog that she had ever seen. He eyed her, then the doughnut. Ever since being tiny, Samantha had been terrified of dogs. Whirling round, she ran as fast as her legs could carry her. She wanted more than anything to go home now . . . home to where she really belonged. They loved her at home. Of course they complained, nagging her about her eating habits and general untidiness, but she knew deep down that they really loved her.

It took Samantha about twenty minutes to reach the safety of her house. At the doorstep she paused and thought with dismay what the family would be thinking about her disappearance. Then she realised that none of them would be up at this time of night, and probably hadn't even noticed her departure. Getting into the house the same way as she had got out, Samantha pushed the flap of the letterbox on number 4, Orchard Avenue and squeezed through it.

At 12.00 pm, after a good meal of corn and grain and a quick preen in her mirror, Samantha the hamster was back on her wheel once more in the little, comfortable cage that Susan Turner had forgotten to lock before she went to bed.

The Witch Next

MRS TINSDALE, the lady who had recently come to live next door to Stacey, was supposed to be a witch. Stacey's mum liked to mention it from time to time.

"She's not an evil, broomstick-flying, witch, you understand," Stacey's mum would say. "She's just an ordinary person with a few very extraordinary powers."

The bit about her being ordinary was true. In fact, apart from having a black cat, as witches were supposed to, Mrs Tinsdale seemed really quite normal to Stacey.

"What does Mrs Tinsdale do exactly?" Stacey was eager to know. "I mean, does she cast spells by the light of the full moon, or what?"

"I'm not too sure," Stacey's mum admitted. "I only know she likes to help people."

"Well, in that case, I expect she'd like to help me," Stacey thought, because she'd already decided she'd like a few changes made in her life.

To begin with, then, there was Stacey's school . . . . . .

"I wish something would happen to my school," Stacey remarked to Mrs Tinsdale one day when they were chatting over the garden fence. "If you feel like casting a spell for me, an earthquake would do — just a small one. Then they'd have to build us a new school with huge windows and those open staircases and everything."

"Oh, but it would be a shame if that lovely, old Victorian building fell down," Mrs Tinsdale replied. "It's full of character, and much more attractive than an ugly concrete-and-glass box."

Stacey hadn't looked at it quite like that before. She had to agree that the school hall did look nice sometimes — when it was all trimmed up for the annual bazaar, for instance, or the harvest festival.

Anyway, it didn't matter too much about the school, because, actually, there was a more important spell Stacey wanted to interest Mrs Tinsdale in.

"There's a girl in our class called Dawn Bassett. I've always wanted her to be my best friend," she said now.

"Maybe she will be one day — if she likes you, that is," replied Mrs Tinsdale, stroking Blackie the cat as he walked along the fence between them.

"That's the trouble," Stacey went on to explain. "Dawn only gets friendly with girls who are fantastic at sport, as she is herself. She's just been made captain of the basketball team. I think basketball's great, but I'm not very good at it."

Stacey stopped speaking to smile at Mrs Tinsdale in what she hoped was a winning way, then she continued: "Perhaps you could get me into the team for the match on Saturday?"

"Perhaps," said Mrs Tinsdale. "Or perhaps you should just practise more."

At the next P.E. lesson, Stacey did her best to be noticed and picked out for the basketball match. But when the team list went up on Friday, Stacey's name wasn't on it.

She stomped home, disappointed and angry. With tears still in her eyes, she knocked on the neighbour's door.

When Mrs Tinsdale answered, Stacey burst out: "I don't believe you're a witch at all! You're a fraud! You're just pretending!" Then she ran away home and hid in her bedroom.

After a time, Stacey simmered down. Then she started to feel ashamed of herself. It wasn't like her to be so ill-mannered. Anyway, what did it matter whether Mrs Tinsdale was really a witch or not? What counted was that she was a friendly person to have as a neighbour.

104

Door

Stacey began to realise what she must do. First, she went out to her own little patch of garden where she picked all the flowers that were in bloom — and some that weren't.

Then she plucked up her courage and took them all — phlox, stocks and marigolds — round to Mrs Tinsdale.

"I'm sorry I was rude," she apologised to Mrs Tinsdale, feeling very small and foolish. "I didn't mean it. Can we be friends again?"

"Of course," said Mrs Tinsdale accepting the bouquet with a delighted smile. "I've forgotten it already. It's a pity

you didn't make the school team. Never mind — everything turns out for the best . . . you'll see. If we try to help others, we often help ourselves as well. Think about it."

STACEY did think about it. She thought about something else, too. How did Mrs Tinsdale come to hear that Stacey hadn't got into the basketball team? News sure did travel fast!

"If we try to help others, we often help ourselves as well." The next morning Stacey took Mrs Tinsdale's advice and went round to the school before the match and volunteered to assist

with the refreshments. She felt quite virtuous because it wasn't a popular job. But Mrs Tinsdale was right — as it turned out, Stacey really enjoyed herself.

Ellie Williamson was helping, too. She was buttering scones and setting out the crockery and she told Stacey exactly what to do without being bossy about it.

To be truthful, Stacey had never particularly liked Ellie Williamson — but now she wondered why. The two of them got on so well and had such a good giggle over the washing-up that Ellie asked Stacey to go to her house in the evening to hear some records.

Really, you found an exciting friend just when you were least expecting it, thought Stacey, as she was getting ready to go out later on.

And she was so happy, she called to tell Mrs Tinsdale before she set off for Ellie's.

"I can't stop," she said, breathless because she was in a hurry. "But I just wanted to tell you that it's a good thing you're not really a witch. Dawn

Bassett flew into a tantrum today because she missed so many baskets and I've gone right off her. And, anyway, I've made a smashing new friend. She's super!"

"That's all right, then," Mrs Tinsdale said in a pleased voice. "'Bye. Have a good time at Ellie's."

It was a couple of minutes before Stacey realised just what Mrs Tinsdale had said. And by that time the door was closed and only Blackie was in the garden. He was stretched along the fence in his favourite spot.

"How did Mrs Tinsdale know about Ellie? I'm almost sure I didn't mention her name," Stacey said to Blackie, as there was no-one else about.

She sighed, mystified, and gave Blackie a little farewell pat as she walked by him towards the gate.

As she turned away, she couldn't be sure whether she was dreaming or if the cat really did wink one huge green eye . . .

The End

GETTING IT TAPED

SARAH WILKINS was one of those people who "couldn't be bothered with things", like helping her widowed mother, for example.

Sarah, the least you could do is tidy your room!

Not now — I'm busy.

Then, one morning—

Somebody at the front door.

Honestly, Sarah! I'm in the middle of cooking. Can't you go?

But Sarah wouldn't.

Oh . . . what's this?

Sarah! It says here you've won first prize in a breakfast cereal competition! A thousand pounds' worth of home video equipment!

WEET-Y-CRUNCH CEREAL

Colour TV set, video recorder, and camera! But it's impossible — we've never bought any Wee........

Shut up, Mother!

It's not our worry if the stupid company's made a mistake! Let them take it all upstairs!

Be careful with it, clumsy idiot!

If only her father were still alive . . . she used to be such a kind, gentle girl.

That evening, Sarah eagerly scanned the TV programmes.

Great! A pop concert by Ricky Wood at seven-thirty! I must record that!

Gaze

107

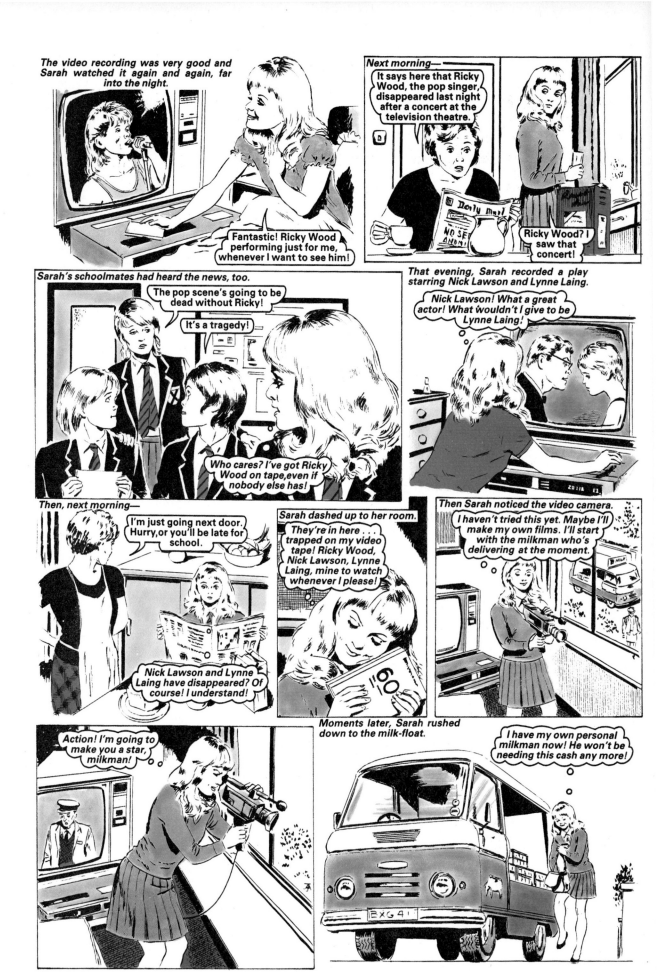

108

Back in her room, Sarah realised that it was getting late.

Mother's coming back and I'm late for school! She'll nag and moan something awful!

Unless I just accidentally point this camera at her!

Sarah's mother was hardly in the house when there was a rap at the door.

The equipment was delivered by mistake? I thought it must have been. You know where it is.

Oh! Sarah's gone off to school and left it running. Still, I suppose you know what to do.

I pointed the camera at myself in the mirror by mistake! Let me out! Let me out!

Shortly afterwards—

I can't say I'm sorry to see it go. It wasn't ours by rights, anyway.

Suddenly, there was a commotion on the front lawn.

Hey, man! What am I doing here?

Nick! What's happened to the studio?

I must be dreaming!

What on earth?

What are all these people doing here? And why are these tapes smashed?

Only three were broken. We still have the fourth.

With your daughter — until she changes her ways!

THE END

109

SNACK LUNCHES

A snack lunch for many, means – every time – just a cheese sandwich. Here are a few easy-to-make, yet simple, recipes that could make lunch-time more interesting.

Always ask an adult before using any electrical or gas appliance — and be very careful, especially when frying. Use either imperial or metric measurements — do not mix.

SUPER SNACK

500 g. (1¼ lb.) mashed potato (use instant potato, if preferred).
1 egg, separated.
Flour.
1 x 225 g. (7.9 oz.) can Heinz Curried Beans with Sultanas.
50 g. (2 oz.) salted peanuts, roughly chopped.
50 g. (2 oz.) Cheddar cheese, grated.
Porridge oats, bran, crushed cornflakes, or other cereal, to coat.
Oil for frying.

Mix the potato and egg yolk, and shape into 8 cakes, using floured hands. Combine the beans, peanuts and cheese, then divide between the potato cakes. Work the potato around the bean mixture to completely encase it. Dip in the beaten egg white, then roll in the chosen cereal. Fry in hot fat for about 5 minutes until crisp and golden. Serve at once with salad. Makes 8.

(Recipe by kind permission of H. J. Heinz Ltd.)

CHEESY APPLES

Ingredients:
¼ cucumber, unpeeled and finely diced.
1 stick celery, washed and finely diced.
4 oz. (100 g.) Edam cheese, finely cubed.
2 oz. (50 g.) black grapes, de-seeded and halved.
4 fl. oz. (100 ml.) low-calorie lemon mayonnaise.
4 red dessert apples.
Dash of cayenne pepper.
Salt and pepper.
Lemon juice.

Method:
Combine cucumber, celery, cheese and grapes with the low-calorie mayonnaise in a bowl. Cut "lids" off the apples, then, using a grapefruit knife or teaspoon, carefully scoop out the flesh without marking the skin. Dice the apple flesh, discard the core, and add to the mayonnaise mixture. Season. Brush inside apple cups and lids with lemon juice. Spoon the salad mixture into the apple cups, and replace the lids at an angle. Makes 4.

(Recipe by kind permission of the Dutch Dairy Bureau.)

POTTED MEAT

50 g. (2 oz.) butter.
225 g. (8 oz.) onions, peeled and chopped.
225 g. (8 oz.) cooked meat — pork, lamb or chicken.
1 x 450 g. (15.9 oz.) can Heinz baked beans.
2 tblsp. chutney.
Salt and pepper.

Melt the butter, add the onions, and cook them gently until soft but not brown.

Mince the cooked meat and onions together, then stir in the beans and chutney. Season the mixture well. Press into a paté dish. Cool for a few hours. Serve as a paté with toast, or as a delicious filling for sandwiches.

(Recipe by kind permission of H. J. Heinz Ltd.)

STUFFED BAKED POTATOES

Try these tasty baked potato recipe ideas from the Colman's Kitchen. Simple to prepare and easy to serve out of doors, these stuffed baked potato recipes make an inexpensive dish for feeding a large party of chums.

Baked Potatoes:

Choose 4 potatoes of about 175 g. (6 oz.) each. Wash well and prick with a fork in several places. Bake in a pre-heated oven of 200° C. (400° F.) Gas Mark 6 for 1-1½ hours until tender. Choose one of each of the following fillings for 4 baked potatoes.

Filling 1:

25 g. (1 oz.) butter.
1 medium onion, skinned and chopped.
100 g. (4 oz.) corned beef, diced.
2 tblsp. Colman's Horseradish Mustard.
Salt and pepper.

Cut the cooked potatoes in half and scoop out the centres. Melt the butter and fry the onion lightly and quickly. Add remaining ingredients, plus the roughly-mashed potato. Spoon back into the potato skins and reheat under the grill, or in the oven.

Filling 2:

200 g. (7 oz.) can pink salmon, skinned and bones removed.
2 tblsp. Colman's Horseradish mustard.
2 tblsp. chopped parsley.
Knob of butter.
Dash of milk.
Salt and pepper.

Cut the cooked potatoes in half and scoop out the centres. Roughly mash the potato and add the remaining ingredients, mixing well. Season to taste. Pile filling back into potato skins and reheat under the grill or in the oven.

Filling 3:

150 ml. (¼ pt.) soured cream.
2 tblsp. Colman's Chive Mustard.
100 g. (4 oz.) Red Leicester cheese, grated.

Cut the cooked potatoes in half and scoop out some of the potato filling leaving a "wall" of about 6 mm. (¼"). (Use spare potato to make mashed potato or for another dish.) Mix together soured cream and mustard and pour into potato skins. Top with grated cheese and bubble under the grill until golden.

(Recipe by kind permission of Colman's of Norwich.)

TALLY-HO! GET YOUR RIDING-GEAR ON! IT'S BEING PLAYED IN TACK-ROOMS EVERYWHERE!

THE GREAT

 **PONY GAME!**

SEE IF YOU'RE LUCKY!

1 PONY

2 SADDLE

3 STABLE

4 FOOD

5 GROOMING KIT

6 TRANSPORT

THE SIX CARDS SHOW THE MAIN ITEMS NEEDED TO BE A PONY OWNER. TO PLAY THE GAME, YOU NEED FOUR SUCH SETS, SO EITHER TRACE THEM OFF ONTO THIN CARD AND CUT OUT, OR MAKE 24 CARDS AND GLUE ON PICS CUT FROM MAGAZINES, ETC. EACH PLAYER ALSO NEEDS THREE TOKENS BUTTONS, COUNTERS, OR WHATEVER.

WHETHER THERE ARE TWO, THREE OR FOUR PLAYERS, USE ALL 24 CARDS, STARTING WITH THEM IN A PACK UPSIDE DOWN ON THE TABLE. EACH PLAYER, IN TURN, TAKES A CARD FROM THE PACK AND PLACES IT FACE UP IN FRONT OF HER, SO THAT ALL PLAYERS CAN SEE ALL THE CARDS IN PLAY. IF YOU DRAW A DUPLICATE CARD, PLACE ON TOP OF THE ONE YOU ALREADY HAVE. THE OBJECT IS TO COLLECT A FULL SET, FIRST ONE TO DO SO BEING THE WINNER.

USE YOUR TOKENS ONE OR TWO AT A TIME BY PLACING IN THE CENTRE, AND, INSTEAD OF TAKING A CARD FROM THE PACK, TAKING ONE OR TWO FROM ANOTHER PLAYER. TOKENS ARE USED NOT ONLY TO OBTAIN CARDS YOU NEED, BUT, MORE IMPORTANTLY, TO STOP ANOTHER PLAYER FROM COMING OUT THAT IS, COMPLETING HER COLLECTION. IN USE OF THE TOKENS LIES THE REAL SECRET OF THE GAME AND THERE'S FAR MORE TO IT THAN AT FIRST MEETS THE EYE!

A SUPER GAME FOR 2, 3, OR 4 RIDERS!

The Wishing Well

You never used to be so awkward, Gillian. What happened to that nice little daughter we used to have?

She's run away and left us with this little monster instead!

Well, if that's true, I wish she'd come back!

No chance! I think we're stuck with this one!

They're being stupid — talking as if I was a little kid!

Well, if Mum does have a nice, little daughter somewhere, I wish she'd come back and get me out of helping at home for just one day!

Huh! What a fool I am to waste good money on a useless wishing well!

Oh, I wouldn't say the wishing well was useless.

Wh-who are you?

I'm Mum's nice, little girl. You wished for me to come, didn't you? Well now I'm going home to help her make the dinner.

I must be seeing things — or I'm dreaming!

Gillian followed her double home.

Shall I peel the potatoes for you, Mum?

Thank you — that would be lovely.

For some reason, Mum can't see me! Probably no-one can!

A little later—

The potatoes are on the stove, Mum. You sit down a minute while I hang out the washing.

Hey, this isn't so bad! I might as well take it easy and let her do all the work, just as I wished!

Later— I've cleaned and tidied my bedroom, Dad. Now, here's a nice cup of tea.

I hope she doesn't overdo it, or they'll expect me to behave like this every day!

Then—

This isn't so good! Nobody can see me, so there isn't any dinner for me! Still, it won't be for much longer.

I'll do the dishes. Why don't you two run along to the funfair? Gillian deserves a treat.

Oh!

At the fair—

I was going to ask Mum to take me to the fair, but now she'll say I've already been!

116

117

DOG'S VERY OWN Amazin'ly Tricky Puzzles

THERE ARE SEVEN ITEMS BELOW. WHICH IS THE ODD ONE OUT?

THIS LITTLE CHAP IS LOST. WHICH PATH SHOULD HE TAKE TO FIND HIS WAY HOME?

HERE'S A SIMPLE WAY TO DRAW DOG.

1.

2.

3.

A B C

ANSWER—
The telephone is the odd one, as all the other items begin with the letter "B".

ANSWER— Path B.

UNSCRAMBLE THE LETTERS ON THIS DOG'S BOWL TO DISCOVER HIS NAME.

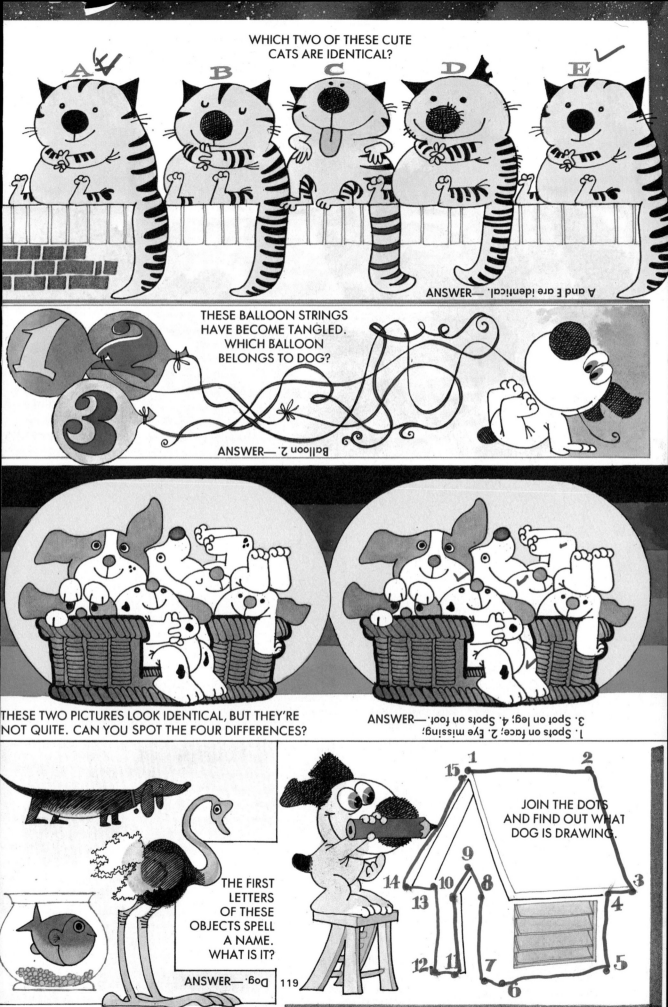

WHICH TWO OF THESE CUTE CATS ARE IDENTICAL?

ANSWER—A and E are identical.

THESE BALLOON STRINGS HAVE BECOME TANGLED. WHICH BALLOON BELONGS TO DOG?

ANSWER—Balloon 2.

THESE TWO PICTURES LOOK IDENTICAL, BUT THEY'RE NOT QUITE. CAN YOU SPOT THE FOUR DIFFERENCES?

ANSWER—1. Spots on face; 2. Eye missing; 3. Spot on leg; 4. Spots on foot.

THE FIRST LETTERS OF THESE OBJECTS SPELL A NAME. WHAT IS IT?

ANSWER—Dog.

JOIN THE DOTS AND FIND OUT WHAT DOG IS DRAWING.

119

PEOPLE 'N' PETS

A SURVEY in the American city of New York shows that people there are keeping some strange household pets. Not content with the usual cats, dogs and cage birds, there are lion cubs, racoons, doves, possums, bees, rabbits, seals, geese, mice, hamsters, frogs, owls, tarantula spiders, cows, goats, leopards, weasels, monkeys, crayfish, porcupines, gorillas, crocodiles and coyotes—and all of them are showered with love and affection.

To prevent his turtle becoming bored swimming around in the tank all day, one man regularly puts it in the bath and simulates a thunderstorm by turning on the shower and switching the light on and off. He claims that the turtle loves it.

But all this isn't new. Archaeologists have found evidence that people treated animals as friends, rather than food, as long as 15,000 years ago.

In ancient Rome, pretty fish were kept in ornamental ponds and it was thought fashionable to breed large eels. One great Roman lady, Antonia, fitted her favourite eel with golden earrings.

Hundreds of years later, King Louis XV of France was so keen on fish that he invented the goldfish bowl so that he could keep his favourites near to him inside the palace. And, later still, a famous British Prime Minister, Sir Winston Churchill, liked to talk to the goldfish he kept in the pond at his home, Chartwell. He would call out to the fish while still out of sight of the pond, and the fish would be waiting at the water's edge for him when he got there.

From earliest days, our Kings and Queens seem to have liked animals, especially dogs. Remember, King Charles II has some spaniels named after him and James I, who didn't get on very well with people, was intensely fond of animals of all kinds. He built a private zoo in St James's Park and was overjoyed when the King of Spain sent him an elephant and five camels.

George IV was another king who treated some of his friends badly, yet was devoted to his pets. When the Pasha of Egypt sent him a giraffe, he had special quarters built and treated it like an honoured guest.

Queen Victoria erected bronze memorials to her pet dogs when they died. Her dogs—just like the present Queen's corgis—must have had a royal life, but few dogs have been so well loved as Flush, the spaniel who belonged to the poet Elizabeth Barrett Browning. Elizabeth was an invalid for most of her life and Flush would keep her company all day in her little room in Wimpole Street.

When the handsome poet Robert Browning began to call to see Elizabeth, Flush became more and more jealous. One day he hid behind the sofa, and, when Robert Browning bent to kiss Elizabeth's hand, Flush darted out and bit the poet's leg. Robert Browning must have forgiven him, for, when the romantic couple eloped to Italy, Flush went with them on their honeymoon and lived with them happily until he died.

It's easy to be fond of a dear little dog, but Sir Walter Raleigh thought there was no more noble animal in the world than his pet pig. A present day pig, Waterhole Ike, who lives with his master in America, is the only pig in the world to have a savings account in its own name. Has he never heard of piggy banks?

Today, there are millions of animals kept as pets all over the world and one doctor claims that the pet you choose shows what kind of person you are. For example, if you own a dog, you are affectionate and generous. Birds mean you are possessive, while cat owners are cool and aloof. If you have a tank of tropical fish, it could mean that you don't make friends easily, but if you own a mouse or a hamster you are innocent and totally trusting.

Where does that leave you if you prefer lizards, snakes or tarantula spiders?

Mother Goose

MOTHER GOOSE kept a small shop selling items from the world of nursery rhymes and fairy tales. She was an expert on the old stories.

"John and Jennie Horner, newly orphaned, were sent to a dreary orphanage in Victorian England."

You have ten guineas, you say? I'll take that, to cover expenses. I am the beadle, Mr Rumbold.

But . . . but . . it was all the money our poor mother left us, sir!

"What a good boy am I!" said Little Jack Horner. And he was, too, but it wasn't a plum he pulled out of his Christmas pie! Here's what really happened . . .

Jennie and John were soon put to work.

You'll soon learn that troublemakers aren't liked here, girl! Put some effort into it!

Yes, Mrs Bindle!

Jennie complained to the housekeeper, Mrs Bindle.

Mrs Bindle, could we not have kept the money? And surely we could have some better food than this?

Ungrateful brats! Eat up — it's all you'll get today!

She and Rumbold starve the children here to line their own pockets!

121

That night, Mrs Bindle and Mr Rumbold enjoyed a splendid dinner, thanks to the twins' ten guineas.

Those Horners are the sort as causes trouble, Mr Rumbold!

Never fear, Mrs Bindle — we'll soon break their spirits here!

Christmas was not far away, but it was not a happy time at the orphanage.

Lady Wilberforce, our benefactress, is visiting us tomorrow. No trouble from you, or it will be the worse for your brother!

She knows I won't give in . . . so she's threatening to hurt John!

Whenever Lady Wilberforce called, the children had a good meal and wore their best clothes.

I'm glad to see the children eating so well. You're doing an excellent job here.

Thank you, Lady Wilberforce! We do our humble best!

Psst! Have you seen Lady Wilberforce's ruby ring?

Indeed I have, Mr Rumbold! It must be worth a small fortune!

After lunch, Lady Wilberforce left.

I'll be back the day after tomorrow — Christmas Day.

We are honoured to entertain you, Lady Wilberforce. Good day, your ladyship.

And, a few minutes later —

What's that, Mr Rumbold?

The ring, Mrs Bindle! the ruby ring! It must have slipped from her ladyship's finger! We shall be rich!

122

123

You eat like an animal! Go and sit in the corner! No more dinner for you!

Jennie had an idea.

Poor little John! She's doing this because she knows I was going to expose her. And John will suffer worse if I try to tell Lady Wilberforce the truth.

This is my last chance! I'll put the ring into the fruit pie!

Then —

Please accept my portion of pie, Lady Wilberforce, for your great generosity in providing this meal.

I shall give it to this little boy in the corner.

You are very kind, my dear, but I won't accept.

Oo! Thank you!

He stole it! I knew it would be the Horners!

There's a great big plum in here! Oh! It's not a plum!

My ring!

A five year old boy, who pulls the ring out in full view of everyone from a piece of pie I handed him myself! You must think me very stupid!

Jennie told what she had seen, and the Bow Street Runners were called.

I suspected that Bindle and Rumbold were swindlers, so I dropped the ring on purpose. Thanks to you, and little John, I discovered the truth!

Until we can find some new staff, you will all come and stay with me at Middleton Hall. I think you'll like it there. I live alone, apart from my servants.

You're almost old enough to go into service, Jennie. I need a new maid. Would you be interested? I'll provide a home for little John, as well.

Indeed I would, Lady Wilberforce!

He certainly was! From Jennie's point of view, he had certainly pulled a real "plum" job out of his Christmas pie!

I've finished my pudding, Jenny!

What a good boy you are, John!

THE END

125